THE FIVE-POINT RESCUE PLAN

By
Christine Mowbray
BSc MCSP AACP HCPC (Registered)
and Dr. Karen Forshaw
MA MB BChir MRCGP

Published by The Solopreneur Publishing Company Ltd.

www.thesolopreneur.co.uk

Medical Disclaimer
The information contained in this book is provided for
education. It is not intended as, and should not be relied
upon as, medical advice. The publisher and authors are not
responsible for any specific health needs that may require
medical supervision. If you have any underlying health
problems or have any doubts about the advice contained in this
book, you should contact a qualified medical, dietary, or other
appropriate professional.

The Solopreneur Publishing Company Ltd focuses on the needs
of each individual author client. This book has been published
through the 'Solopreneur Self-Publishing (SSP)' brand that
enables authors to have complete control over their finished
book whilst utilising the expert advice and services usually
reserved for traditionally published print, in order to produce an
attractive, engaging, quality product. Please note, however, that
final editorial decisions and approval rested with the author.
The publisher takes no responsibility for the accuracy of the
content.

ISBN 978-0-9957520-3-0

Printed in the U.K.

ABOUT THE AUTHORS
Chrissie Mowbray BSc MCSP AACP HCPC (Registered)

The first Five-Point Rescue plan I made was my own. As a young physiotherapist I suffered with eczema on my hands. My plan cured me. From then on I knew I could use this method to help myself and others.

I qualified as a physiotherapist in 1993 and worked in all departments of the hospital and outpatients gaining experience with every patient group from intensive care to the gymnasium.

In 1995, I specialised in Adult Learning Disabilities and Paediatrics. I also became experienced in working with clients with challenging behaviour and mental health problems.

In this role, I worked extensively with patients, carers, and families to assist in the management of complex physical and emotional problems. Because our clients often experienced difficulty in understanding and expressing themselves, we were unable to use the conventional techniques used by physiotherapists to achieve our objectives.

We, therefore, used a wide and imaginative range of therapies to assist our clients. This type of therapy was often seen as unconventional as all of the work we did was brilliant fun.

We were treating the whole person for all of their emotional and physical needs rather than concentrating on single body parts. This is where I really began to appreciate the value of working holistically.

I worked closely with a wide variety of health professionals with a similar ethos as part of a multidisciplinary team.

In 1998 I trained as a hypnotherapist and worked privately from my own home helping people with various issues including emotional trauma, PTSD due to abuse, low self-esteem, weight loss, addiction, and phobia.

I currently work as a physiotherapist in a thriving private clinic which I run with my husband.

We have an extremely busy and varied caseload and pride ourselves in dealing with the most complex cases. Often people come to us with chronic pain and debilitating conditions and have been through the NHS referral system. On many occasions, they have received a diagnosis and the appropriate medication and advice but are struggling to manage their pain or dysfunction on a daily basis. They come to us in search of some physical treatment which will alleviate their symptoms. Their needs are usually more complex than that, but it's a good place to start!

I have a wide variety of therapeutic skills in my tool belt including acupuncture, myofascial release, and mechanical techniques but I have always found that it is the combination of physical treatment and a very specific kind of strategic counselling which work best. That strategic counselling is the backbone of the techniques in this book.

Throughout my training, I had always had the feeling that mind and body could not be separated and that the state of one was intrinsically linked to the other. Throughout my varied career as a therapist, I have never encountered anything to persuade me otherwise.

I am also the mother of three children two of whom are now teenagers, one of whom is actually an adult! When I first met Karen we were the two mums at toddler group who could not seem to get organised. It was clear immediately that we shared common values and both worked in a very similar way. We were both operating a system where the focus was on enabling the patient to take control of their pain, whether physical or emotional and manage their own situation. This book is the result of our sharing, honing and perfecting our methods.

I really hope that this book galvanises you into a positive change as much as writing it has done for us.

Love and light.
Chrissie.

To contact Christine Mowbray
email her on - info@belllanephysiotherapy.co.uk

Dr. Karen Forshaw MA MB BChir MRCGP

A week before my 14th birthday I was knocked over and spent the next six weeks in the hospital. This experience had a profound, lasting effect on me; the kindness and caring of the Doctors and Nurses inspired me to become a Doctor myself so that I could help others in the same way.

Whilst at medical school in Cambridge it became clear to me that General Practice was the way to achieve my goal. I was drawn to this holistic specialty that allows Doctors to see people as human beings rather than diseases. I wanted to be a part of people's lives, seeing them through bad times and helping where possible.

I am now a GP Partner in an ex-mining community in South Yorkshire. As well as seeing patients I teach young doctors who are training to be GPs. I try to instil in them the qualities and strengths I think are paramount– kindness and empathy in hand with good clinical knowledge.

I organise the ongoing continuing professional development for all the GPs in my area, and I am a GP Appraiser, helping qualified GPs improve their standards and performance.

My clinical role is very challenging as the social deprivation in the area can impact on people's health; a holistic overview considering a person's health beliefs and personal circumstances is essential. In my experience, most health problems have a psychological basis, and so medication alone is never going to be the answer.

My years of consulting and teaching have given me a unique perspective on the importance of helping people develop techniques that empower them to take control of their situation and improve their physical and mental health. Time after time people have come to me asking me to "fix" them. My response has always been to help them "fix" themselves.

Chrissie and I met over a decade ago at a Mums and Toddler group. Over the years we have helped each other through personal and professional challenges. We were drawn together because we were always the Mums who were late or never had a tissue when needed! Over time we came to realise that our approaches to treating people were the same. We developed specific skills that allowed us to help people become stronger and more confident in managing their symptoms and controlling and solving their problems.

We truly believe our methods work and can have lasting benefits for people. We see this daily with our patients, and this gives us enormous job satisfaction. However, we came to realise that we had limited reach and were only helping the people who came to see us. From this realisation, our book was born. Our Five-Point Rescue Plan available to all.

I hope you find the book inspiring and that it makes you stronger in mind and body.

With Love
Karen

To contact Dr. Karen Forshaw
email her on – Karen.forshaw1@nhs.net

CONTENTS

"The world we have created is a product of our thinking; it cannot be changed without changing our thinking"

Albert Einstein

Introduction

Rescue Yourself from Anything

This book describes a refreshing, new approach to counselling, which focuses on empowerment of the individual.

It aims to avoid the kind of circular thinking that can lead to people becoming stuck in the negativity of their situation.

Following the Five-Point Rescue Plan enables you to take control and move forward.

It is a practical guide to addressing any difficult situation which life may have thrown at you.

Examples of such problems include:

Stress

Pain

Illness

Money worries

Insomnia

Relationship problems

Addiction

Abuse

Caring for others

Bereavement

Lack of self-worth

Negative body image

Terminal illness

In fact, there is no single problem that the plan outlined in this book will not address.

In the next few chapters, we will clearly show you how to develop your own tailor-made plan to rescue yourself from anything!

"No one saves us but ourselves.

No one can and no one may.

We ourselves must walk the path."

Buddha

Chapter One

Philosophy of the Five-Point Rescue Plan

We are a Physiotherapist and a General Practitioner who qualified in 1993 and 1999 respectively.

We have a combined clinical experience of over 40 years working in a wide variety of settings with the general public.

The basic principle behind this book is self-management.

It presented itself to us whilst we were discussing and comparing our own experiences as clinicians.

During our work, we realised that we encountered a wide variety of complex physical, psychological and social problems, and were often giving similar patterns of advice to our patients.

What varied was the detail, but the principles of strategy were common to each problem.

The idea slowly took shape over many years of interacting with patients in clinic.

Invariably their needs were complex.

Often the issue that they felt was troubling them was actually clouded by another.

Example

When patients attend for physiotherapy, one of the most common problems they present with is pain. We noticed when taking the time to listen to our patients that the pain was much easier to bear when additional aspects of the situation were addressed, e.g. increased understanding of important family members, practical solutions to mobility problems, etc.

Once we had identified what was similar in each of the management strategies we had helped patients to create, we then began to apply it to other situations, those presented to us by patients and those in our own lives too.

It was during this process that we realised that we could adapt our model of "Five Points of Rescue" to any situation that either of us brought to the table.

This included a full spectrum of problems from the simplest, to the darkest and most complicated scenarios.

In the beginning, as clinicians, we were intuitively assisting people in formulating solutions to their problems.

It is in our nature and training to do so.

Over time and with experience and study of the process, the Five-Point Rescue Plan began to emerge.

The process continues to evolve to this day.

Through regular interaction with people, facilitating their formulation of a Five-Point Rescue Plan, we find that they continually contribute to the strategy and our understanding of it.

As patients are actively involved, they have helped with the development of the strategy.

In fact the term "rescue points" was actually coined by a patient with low back pain who had been asked, during a recurrence of her pain, to go back to her plan and look at her points.

When dealing with problems, people are usually

advised to develop coping strategies to help.

However, people are rarely offered any practical advice on how to do so.

Some turn to unhealthy options such as drugs and alcohol.

Externally, and with hindsight, it is easy to see that certain coping mechanisms are destructive and can even become a problem in their own right.

People cope the best way that they can but often get stuck in their situation, and it becomes difficult to see the light at the end of the tunnel.

In writing this book, we aim to give you the skills to work through your set of issues identifying which factors you can change, and which you cannot.

We will help you develop your own appropriate coping strategies.

This will empower you and allow you to become independent of other people and of any emotional crutch.

You owe yourself the best possible outcome of any situation and you can have it if you master the Five-Point Rescue Plan!

You may have been bombarded with advice, information and sometimes pills and potions.

Some of these may help, but often not.

The reason for this is simple - the person giving the advice is not you!

Nobody but you can truly understand the details of your predicament or the ultimate effect of it on you and those around you.

The treatments you are offered are studied and devised by panels of experts, but they are generalised, not specific to you.

You, on the other hand, are an expert on you!

Your view of the world is unique.

You have specific likes and dislikes, a set of values instilled from childhood.

You have learned throughout your life from a series of experiences that are totally individual to you.

It is critical that this view, your view, is at the foundation of any management plan.

If not, then the plan is unlikely to succeed

because you are not invested in it and have no real responsibility to make it work.

The Five-Point Rescue Plan is all about you.

It puts the responsibility back where it belongs, in the hands of the only person who can really do anything about your situation, which, of course, is you.

Many people feel they cannot help themselves and become so tangled up in their situation that it is hard to see any way out.

With this book we are going to bridge the gap between you and the Healthcare Professionals, combining your expertise with theirs.

This will allow you to take control of your situation rather than sit on the sidelines as a spectator.

Gaining control is very empowering and has a positive effect on your mental health.

Research shows, and we all know from our own experiences, that mental and physical health are intrinsically linked (Miller, 1992).

Simply put; if the physical health improves, so does the mental health and vice versa.

Learn to use this book, and we guarantee benefits to both.

Whether you are dealing with an ongoing problem or a sudden, unexpected crisis, there is usually no individual solution that will ease you out of your situation.

Often people put all their hope in one single answer believing it to be their salvation.

This invariably leads to a succession of failures and disappointments, compounding the problem.

Example

Patients have approached us because they wish to try acupuncture for their pain. This has often come about because the patient has tried everything else, or someone they know has experienced miraculous relief. They come in the hope that this will be their salvation. It is very rare, in a clinic where we look at our patients holistically, that we will give just acupuncture.

What has been seen to work in these situations is the whole process. This includes a thorough assessment, counselling, postural advice, appropriate physical techniques, exercises, and acupuncture. The combination of treatments has had the positive effect, not just one.

We have known patients to request a particular course of treatment which was, on assessment, found to be unsuitable for them and could not be given; after a Five-Point Rescue Plan was put in place, those patients were no longer looking for a miracle cure.

From our many years of clinical experience, we have discovered two things.

Firstly, you must focus on what you can change rather than what limits you.

Secondly, it is the implementation of a prescribed *combination* of strategies that work to help you solve your problems.

It is important to remember, however, that making massive changes is not sensible or sustainable.

Radical changes in habit are hard to maintain because they are unfamiliar to us.

They may be relatively easy to apply at first, whilst the motivation to change is at its greatest, but if success is not achieved quickly, we often revert back to our previous more comfortable habits.

In short, the closer changes are to our current lifestyle and routine, the greater the chance of success.

Example

Lindsey had put on weight after having children and was very unhappy about this. She had tried diet after diet to no avail. Each time a new technique became popular, she gave it a go and stuck to the rules of the diet religiously for the first two weeks. Initially, she would see positive results then invariably something would happen in her busy life that meant she couldn't follow the plan. The weight loss, of course, faltered. This left her feeling low and ashamed of herself, which led to comfort eating, thereby, compounding her problem. After talking things through, she realised the diets she followed were unrealistic given her lifestyle. Instead, via her Five-Point Rescue Plan, she established several small changes that were sustainable. This allowed her to maintain the changes for several weeks and she reached her target weight.

Your Five-Point Rescue Plan will enable you to concentrate on the things you can change, and modify your current situation to create a new and more desirable one, despite your limitations.

With this book, you will learn how to develop your own specific Five-Point Rescue Plan for any situation or problem that arises in your life.

To be successful, your plan must contain as much of you and your individual situation as possible.

Your plan will allow you to develop your own bespoke coping strategies.

You will be able to take control of any problem with positivity and self-confidence.

Health and happiness will be in the palm of your hand.

The process requires honesty, perseverance, and self-discipline; but the results are hugely gratifying.

To continue with humour and humility is advised.

We look forward to working with you.

"The greatest discovery of all time is that a person can change his future by merely changing his attitude."

Oprah Winfrey

Chapter Two

The Five-Point Rescue Plan

We described previously that single strategies are prone to failure.

Your task is to create a Five-Point Rescue Plan.

This will consist of a number of strategies or "points of rescue" which you must put in place.

You will need five points of rescue.

Why Five?

- Look at your hand. There are five digits. You will be able to use it as a physical prompt. Each digit will represent one of your points. This will help you visualise and remember your Five-Point Rescue Plan. You can take this with you in the palm of your hand. A handful of points!

- We have found, in practise, that five works because once the reader has implemented the first three points, they begin to feel positive results. This leads to an increased motivation to apply the other two, thus ensuring that all opportunities for improvement are covered.

You must implement and live with your five points.

Weave your Five-Point Rescue Plan into your life, make it part of you and you will reap the benefits.

This should be an enjoyable process because you are taking control of your situation rather than letting it control you.

Follow the step by step guide below to create your own Five-Point Rescue Plan.

Creating Your Five-Point Rescue Plan

There are four steps to creating your Five-Point Rescue Plan.

1. Identify your Problem

Before you start, it is imperative that you take a really good look at what the problem actually is.

From our experience, it isn't always the one you see right in front of you.

Example

Joan comes into clinic complaining of knee pain. She has made the appointment because she is about to go on holiday. She would have put up with the pain otherwise, but she is very distressed because she fears that it will ruin her trip. The biggest problem here is not Joan's pain, but her fear of its potential effect on her holiday. In this scenario, a Five-Point Rescue Plan is put in place with Joan's holiday in mind, and her distress diminishes. She is also treated appropriately for her knee pain.

Another example:

Example

Susan comes to the clinic complaining of migraines. On the surface this is the problem and she could be encouraged to develop a Five-Point Rescue Plan to manage her headaches. It turns out, however, that she is not sleeping because she is worried that her husband is having an affair. She thinks this because he seems to be behaving differently towards her and appears to be distracted all the time. Her constant worry and poor sleep are triggering her migraines. In this case, the underlying problem is not the headaches or the poor sleep. It is a lack of effective communication in her relationship. She establishes a Five-Point Rescue Plan to improve communication and discovers that her husband is in fact worried about being made redundant. This explains his behaviour, Susan's anxiety is reduced, her sleep improves and her migraines settle.

As the examples illustrate; the most obvious problem is not always the one which requires attention first.

It is very important to take the time to analyse your whole situation.

To do this, you have to be really honest with yourself.

It is your issue, and you must own every facet of it, even the bits you don't want to look at.

You must also avoid blame and judgement of others, but most importantly of yourself.

Do not become a victim of your situation.

This leaves you helpless and removes responsibility.

It hinders your ability to take control and to choose what happens.

It is very common to find yourself resisting taking action.

If you find yourself reluctant to start, for a variety

of reasons, then this is your first issue and needs its own five points.

Only then can you see and manage what is really there.

For more on resistance see Troubleshooting (Chapter 3).

Here it may be useful to enlist the help of a trusted friend.

Ideally, this person will empathise with you but will not simply tell you what you are hoping to hear.

Know that it is human nature to relentlessly throw obstacles into your own path.

With this in mind, if part of your problem is of your own making, you may need to find ways to accept this uncomfortable possibility.

Ask your friend for their view of your situation.

Make sure that they are not too close to the problem themselves as they may unconsciously influence you in some way.

You are not asking for their advice.

You do not have to accept everything that is said.

Weigh it up and remember to be honest with yourself.

Be careful here, however, as while talking things over with a friend can provide a satisfying release of emotions and help you to see things differently, it is important to be able to recognise when this becomes moaning or complaining.

Both of these can provide some temporary therapeutic satisfaction, but it is wise to avoid repetitive, negative conversations during which you affirm your helplessness and blame others or events beyond control.

As mentioned before, this removes responsibility and control from you.

If you are enjoying constant support from friends who want a good outcome for you, but you are moaning without taking action, you will soon find those friendships compromised.

Alternatively, you may find it helpful to write your thoughts down on paper, making notes and references to each aspect of the situation.

You may wish to include tables, lists or diagrams to help you to visualise the situation in more depth.

The very act of writing everything down is useful in allowing your thoughts to crystallise, and reading the whole thing back enables you to view it from a slightly different vantage point.

Even though you wrote it, you can achieve some emotional detachment.

Use whichever method works for you.

Here is how to start identifying your problem.

Choose an appropriate time when you are not rushed or busy with other things.

Ask yourself or discuss with a friend, if comfortable, the following questions:

- **Why am I stuck?**

Put simply, what is the cause of my unhappiness?

You are likely to have an immediate answer to this.

Once you have an answer, try to further explore the emotions which relate to your answer.

How does this problem make you feel?

Why do you feel like this?

Keep exploring until you arrive at the issue you feel is at the heart of the matter.

This is a good place to start to affect change.

Example

I am in debt. Why am I in debt? I am in debt because I spend money that I do not have without thinking about it. What causes me to spend money? How do I feel when I spend? How does this habit make me feel generally? Does spending money make me feel happy? Am I unhappy otherwise? Why am I unhappy?

Here the problem may ultimately be the lack of money awareness and budgeting skills.

This behaviour can be changed with a strategic Five-Point Rescue Plan.

However, the above person may be spending for other reasons, such as to temporarily alleviate low self-esteem or depression.

Without pressing the issue and asking "Why?" he/she cannot tailor an appropriate Five-Point Rescue Plan to address the debt, because the issue of self-esteem or depression must be addressed first.

Example

Why am I unhappy? I am overweight. Why am I overweight? I am overweight because I overeat and cannot stop. Why do I overeat? I overeat because I am unhappy!

Here the person in question has looped back to the original problem.

This circular thinking can be overwhelming and stops people moving forwards and helping themselves.

The key to breaking the cycle is to look carefully at the answers.

Unhappiness and being overweight are again symptoms of the problem.

Overeating is the negative behaviour generated by the problem.

The reason for overeating could be one or more of many things such as loneliness, low self-esteem, relationship problems, or negative eating habits established in childhood.

This is what needs to be examined.

Once the true problem is identified, it can be addressed with a specific Five-Point Rescue Plan.

If you are stuck, try looking at your problem from a different perspective.

Ask close friends or relatives what they think.

There may be something obvious that you have not recognised.

If you cannot get to the bottom of it, consider seeking professional help to break the cycle to identify your true problem.

Remember, the things you cannot change are not your problems they are your limitations, and these are addressed below.

- **Did something happen beyond my control?**

The answer to this is most probably "Yes."

We do not exist in a vacuum; we are a part of society and many external factors affect our lives.

We, therefore, often find ourselves in a situation

that is not of our choosing.

The key is to remember that whilst you cannot change what has happened so far, you do have complete control over how you choose to deal with the present situation.

In fact, the only things you can control or change are your thoughts, behaviours and responses within the current circumstances.

Begin by accepting this.

You will find that when you master your own thoughts and behaviours within a situation, things will change around you for the better.

There will always be an ideal set of choices and reactions to produce the most positive outcome within the limitations of your situation.

Learn to make those choices and thereby facilitate the best outcome for you.

If an individual bothers you, you must deal with your own reactions and responses first.

Fix this, and the situation will improve.

This point is illustrated further a little later on under the heading: "Who affects my situation?"

- **What are my limitations?**

You will not like these.

The limitations often initially appear to be 'the problem.'

They are the factors which stop you from achieving your ideal situation.

You must work with and accept them in order to move forward.

They may be set in stone, for example terminal illness, bereavement, divorce or redundancy.

They may be, potentially, influenced by your actions, for example weight issues, debt or relationship problems.

Take some time to explore them.

Know your enemy!

Do not focus on the worst case scenario, but make sure you can look it in the eye.

Ignoring the situation will never be productive and will, in fact, make things worse.

You must acknowledge and understand your

limitations in order to move forwards.

Remember; concentrate on the things that you can change rather than your limitations.

- **What stops me from moving forward?**

These factors are different to your limitations.

Things that stop you moving forward involve the feelings and emotions surrounding your issues.

This applies to you and those around you.

They include your emotional attachment to the outcome, what you want and hope for, what you cannot change, your sadness, your fears and what you do not want to let go of.

Example

Bill has been suffering from a prolonged illness and has received much-needed support from friends and family when unwell. This care and attention provided a lifeline of comfort during a time of fear and pain. On the slow, difficult return to full health, he is reluctant to take the advice he has been given regarding his rehabilitation. He provides many reasons why he is unable to do his exercises and take his prescribed medication.

His mood becomes low, and his progress slows. He subconsciously fears that the much-valued attention from his loved ones will be withdrawn when he is fully recovered. He therefore, subconsciously derails his recovery creating an on-going need for support. Once this fear is recognised and addressed, measures can be put in place to address issues of loneliness and maintain an appropriate level of support. He can then move forward towards a full recovery.

Again you need to be very honest here about the emotions involved.

If you are struggling, try to step out of the situation to gain a more balanced perspective.

What do you really want to happen?

We are all bound to our issues by emotions, attitudes, and beliefs.

This complicated issue is covered in greater detail in Troubleshooting (Chapter 3).

- **Who affects my situation?**

We fulfil many complex roles for the other people in our lives.

These may include; partner, son/daughter, mother/father, friend, colleague, patient, teacher, student, etc.

Those people, in turn, play similar roles in our lives.

We feel responsible for the effect that our situation has on others.

We can never know how someone else is truly feeling, so we imagine how we would feel if we were them.

We then adjust our own behaviour within the situation hoping to manage the emotions of others.

It is in our nature to do this, however, it is not effective in improving the situation.

This is because our responses are based on our own unique model of the world which is shaped by our genetic make-up and experiences.

We cannot fully see or understand another person's model of the world and so we may potentially misjudge their emotions and further complicate the issue.

This is particularly true where children are involved.

If we have to deliver bad news to the children in our lives, we are likely to assume that they will be upset and so deliver the news in a way that will minimise this.

Each child will process bad news differently.

They look to the adults closest to them when learning how to respond.

We must be careful not to create responses within our children just because we expect them.

Example

James falls over in the playground. Before he can react, his mother rushes over assuming he is hurt. In response to this James cries and is more aware of the pain of his grazed knee. The next time he falls in the playground his learned response is to cry.

Human relationships are very complex and will certainly have some kind of impact on any situation.

They will also affect how you respond to the circumstances you find yourself in.

It is important to be aware that these relationships exist and to respect them.

It is also important to acknowledge their impact on your own choices.

Example

During a difficult marital separation, deciding what proportion of time the children spend with parents and grandparents from both sides is a highly emotional situation. There are usually many invested parties whose behaviour, towards others, may well be compromised by events that have taken place during the break-up. Relationships may have broken down giving rise to conflict. Members of the group may be fearful of losing contact with children. They may also fear others influencing the children negatively against them. During a situation like this, we are likely to assume that the child involved is feeling just as we would if we were them. We may then adjust our behaviour with this in mind, complicating things further. We may also behave defensively, through fear, to ensure our own place in the children's future. These behaviours are potentially very damaging to all parties and limit the potential for a positive outcome.

In most situations seeking to change the behaviour of others is fruitless.

The people around you will either react as you want them to, or they won't.

They alone have the responsibility to choose how this goes for them.

This is not for you to engineer.

In contrast, you have complete control over what you say and do.

You can strive to think positively, and you can absolutely choose not to be upset by what others may say or do.

This is true empowerment, and when you conquer this, the negative behaviour of others will stop.

Example

Joanne is the subject of bullying but is unsure as to how to stop it from happening, and so does nothing. Changing the behaviour of the perpetrator would be difficult and ultimately pointless. It is her response to the behaviour, up to now, that has allowed the bullying to become established. It is this that needs to change so that the situation can no longer flourish. She must look to her own behaviour to affect a change otherwise it will continue to be a problem. This kind of action may involve responding to any communication differently during an incident or reporting the problem to someone else. The nature of the change will be individual to the situation and may prove to be emotionally challenging. It often involves examining why you are allowing someone's behaviour to make you feel a certain way. This is taking responsibility for the situation and ultimately gaining control of it.

Professional help may be useful in addressing your own emotional needs, such as restoring self-esteem and confidence.

Mediation and advocacy between the involved parties, in this case, may also prove useful.

What is certain here is that the responsibility for change lies with the person who wishes to affect it.

It may be useful to write a list of those people affected by, or influential in, your situation.

You can also make notes about the roles that those people play and how you think the issues look from their viewpoint.

This will help you to see what judgements you may have made regarding the perspective of other parties.

It will enable you to step back and take a more balanced view of the situation as a whole.

Now go back and look at your answers.

- Consolidate your thoughts and come up with a list of your limitations and a list of issues you can address.
- Prioritise in order of importance to you.
- Prioritise in order of ease of change.

Put them into a table to help you pick out the thoughts, feelings, and behaviours involved.

It might look something like this...

What is my perceived problem?	Examples: I am in debt, I am overweight, I am in pain, I have a physical condition and I can't sleep.
What are my negative behaviours?	Examples: I overeat, I overspend, I complain, I worry.

What drives these behaviours?	Examples: Fear, anger, boredom, unhappiness, envy, greed, apathy, ego, guilt.
What are my limitations?	Examples: My diagnosis, past experiences, the behaviour of others including friends, family and health professionals, time, finances.
What can I change?	Examples: What I think and how I feel. Positive thoughts and feelings generate positive behaviours.
What is my actual problem?	Examples: Low self-esteem, depression, communication problems, low self-worth, lack of purpose.

Look at your table.

Accept your limitations; you cannot change these.

Focus on the problems you have identified.

Now, start by instinctively choosing the problem that jumps out at you.

This is your starting point.

You are now ready to move on and get your Five-Point Rescue Plan started.

2. Choosing Your Points of Rescue

Now that you have decided which problem needs to be addressed first, you need to choose your five specific points of rescue.

Points of rescue are helpful strategies which you are going to easily work into your life to modify the situation you are in.

You are creating a very detailed, problem specific, plan to move you forward through your situation in the most positive way.

It is therefore imperative that you take some time to carefully consider the points of rescue which are going to help you to address your chosen problem.

Your plan will be easier to stick to and more effective if you know you will use your points and that they are tailored to you.

The first points you choose might not be the ones you stick with, but you will learn what works as you go through the process.

The plan will evolve as you practise it and begin to own it.

It is your wise old friend, and it will give you both the push and the comfort that you need to keep going.

The important thing is to make a start and go from there.

Do not be under the impression that this will be complicated and difficult to undertake.

You are already in a difficult situation; this will enable you to navigate your way through it.

Just embarking on the process will improve your ability to see the nature of the issue more clearly and approach it practically.

Taking positive steps to improve things will make you "feel better already" and that is before you even start with the good stuff.

A word of warning; it is possible, at times, to become so overwhelmed by the number of things that you have to do that you do not know where to start.

Here you might fall into the trap of doing nothing.

Simply writing a list of jobs that need to be done often alleviates the anxiety and makes you feel better.

Unfortunately, upon feeling better, you may then happily put away the list without actually doing the necessary work.

In the same way, just because you feel more positive about your situation, do not be deterred or distracted from formulating your plan.

Use the sections below to help you come up with your points.

- **Your points must be relevant to your problem**

Of course, this goes without saying.

If your points do not change the status quo of your situation, then they will not work.

It is also worth noting that they need to be appropriate for your problem.

For example, you may be struggling with

alcoholism, in which case a glass of wine would be entirely detrimental.

If, however, you are facing a terminal diagnosis and enjoy a glass of wine it may be the one thing (in moderation) which gets you through the evening after a difficult, but necessary, family discussion.

- **They must be easy to implement and sustainable**

As we discussed, when explaining the philosophy of The Five-Point Rescue Plan, solutions to problems often fail because they represent massive changes.

These are not sustainable and so lead to failure.

Points that do not take into consideration your likes and dislikes are likewise, doomed.

Take some time to think about who you really are.

Strip away the roles that you play in other people's lives, for example, child, parent, sibling, partner, friend, colleague, patient, etc.

Are you a thinker or a doer?

Are you a listener or a talker?

Can you sit still or do you prefer to be busy?

Do you create or appreciate the creations of others?

Keep this in mind when choosing your points, as keeping them relevant will make them easier to implement and sustain.

Example

If your aim is to lose weight, but you hate exercise, do not choose to go to the gym every day because it will not be achievable. Instead, plan fun activities with friends that incorporate exercise e.g. a night out dancing or an active trip to the park with your children and/or the dog.

- **Your points may be 'old friends' that you already use**

Look realistically at the coping strategies you have in place now.

They may not be ideal, but they have got you this far.

They can be a starting point.

Some careful thought can adapt and improve them so that they become more positive and healthy.

Putting them in place is no problem because they are already there.

Obviously, some coping strategies such as drugs and alcohol are not something we would ever advocate.

Please note that there is a difference between a social drink to help you unwind and alcoholism.

This, however, can be an unpredictable and a slippery slope.

Everything relates to the situation in which you find yourself.

Most of us have a deep understanding of

whether something is helping us or whether it is destructive.

Often the challenge is to know ourselves well and having the courage to be completely honest.

We must balance this with a good deal of self-respect and nurture.

It is often in our nature to be harder on ourselves than we are on others.

You have a responsibility to carry yourself as gently and protectively as possible through this situation, keeping damage to a minimum.

There are enough external factors which can hurt us; we do not need to add to that by beating ourselves up as well!

- **Your points should be easy to fit into your routine**

Whatever your problem your points need to fit into your lifestyle because if you are going to change your situation for the better, they need to become ingrained.

When people are encouraged to change their lifestyle to maintain their health or aid in weight loss, they are advised to use multiple small sustainable steps.

Please see Lindsey's example in Chapter 1.

- **Consider your points a source of comfort**

In times of crisis, routine and ritual are very therapeutic.

Patients who have cared for terminally ill relatives

often comment that they treasured the simple moments: sharing tea, shopping for someone, bathing, or cooking.

Adding structure to your day has a positive effect on your mood.

Even in unimaginably dark times, simply getting dressed and brushing your teeth, no matter how little you want to do so, can set you on a better path.

Your points can add structure and purpose.

Adding structure can also be one of your points!

Examples:

Here we will give some examples of common points chosen by people with particular problems.

The purpose of this is to demonstrate how the plan may be adapted to any situation.

We do not aim to give you your 'Rescue Points' as these will be much more effective if you generate them yourself.

A person suffering from chronic pain may choose five of the following:

- Application of ice/heat to the area (if appropriate).
- Performing prescribed exercises.
- Taking appropriate pain relief.
- Visiting a physiotherapist for treatment and advice.
- Learning about the condition and avoiding activities which aggravate it.
- Join a society for people with a similar condition.
- Acupuncture.
- TENS machine.

- See your GP to discuss a Pain clinic referral.
- Gentle exercise – little and often – join a walking club.

A person with symptoms indicating a serious medical problem, who is fearful of an unpleasant diagnosis, may choose five of the following:

- Discussing the issue with a friend or close family member.
- Visiting the GP for advice and support regarding the way forward.
- Maintaining daily routine as much as possible.
- Engaging in regular pleasant social activity.
- Taking steps to improve general health e.g. diet.
- Relaxation exercises.
- Take time to enjoy the positives in your life e.g. family.
- Engage in activities you usually feel you don't have time for e.g. painting, reading.
- Pampering.

- Retail therapy (as funds allow).

A person suffering from work-related stress may choose five of the following:

- Regular meetings with manager/mentor.
- Consider reducing hours/job share.
- Planning activities/socialising outside of work.
- Planning time for rest or meditation.
- Planning time for management of workload.
- Discuss the situation with close friends or family.
- Counselling.
- Consider seeing your GP.
- Consider a career change.
- Consider Further Education.

A person wishing to lose weight may choose five of the following:

- Regular but fun exercise (of own choice).
- Structured meal planning, including desired

foods.

- Teaming up with a friend in a similar position.
- A weight loss group.
- Factoring in rewards for success.
- Avoid alcohol at least during the week.
- Reduce portion size.
- Avoid eating late at night.
- Drink more water.
- Consider speaking to your GP.

During our discussions regarding the versatility of this plan, we explored some dark scenarios.

No-one wants to imagine how they would react if they were given a terminal diagnosis by their doctor.

This is a time when there appears to be no hope of a positive outcome, and we would not pretend that anything in the plan would offer comfort straight away.

After an event like this, however, there comes a measure of acceptance and an awareness that the diagnosis is here to stay and cannot be changed.

It is at this point where you can begin to look at your choices.

Although the limitations are vast, choices must be made, and you can, at least, control these.

So; a person facing a terminal diagnosis may choose five of the following:

- Getting their financial affairs in order to lessen the impact on loved ones.
- Planning where to have palliative care at the end their life.
- Making a list of things to see and do before end of life.
- Counselling and preparing loved ones (particularly children) in a loving way so as to

dispel fear.

- Have a thorough discussion and consultation regarding end of life pathways, including medication such as pain relief.
- Get Macmillan support.
- Visit the Hospice.
- Talk to people in a similar position.
- Keep communication channels open with family and friends.
- Nominate an advocate to help discuss difficult topics.

3. Put Your Points of Rescue into Practice

The examples of points listed above look a lot like common sense.

They are likely to be similar to much of the advice given by health professionals, family, friends or colleagues during times of crisis.

Formulating a Five-Point Rescue Plan is the process of deliberately selecting five tailor-made points and incorporating them into your life with gentle discipline.

This produces the desired change.

They may not all be things that you do every day.

Taking the first example; if you are in chronic pain and one of your points is to visit your physiotherapist for treatment, the chances are that you will not be able to do that immediately, so you make the appointment and address the other points.

You may benefit from discussing your points with someone who knows you and your situation well.

It is wise to write them down and make them readily accessible.

Put them in your phone, on the fridge, in your diary or by your bed.

Do not put them in a drawer and forget about them.

Having them visible keeps them in your consciousness.

Remember to visualise your hand; one point for

each digit.

There is a certain amount of self-discipline involved.

When one is in crisis, the temptation can be to give in and abandon all self-management.

This is the point when you may claim that it isn't working for you, or that your situation is just too complicated or limited or hopeless.

At this point, we would gently encourage you to come back to your five points and ask yourself if you have addressed them all.

If you haven't then you must before you can reassess the situation.

Once you have selected your points and worked them into your routine, or acted upon them, you

MUST emotionally detach from the issue.

This is an essential part of the process.

You have taken action.

Now you must let everything take its course.

The energy that has been taken up in constantly turning the problem around in your mind must now be utilised in applying your five points of rescue.

Depending on your situation, you may now be able to regain some sense of normality, and respite from the crisis.

During a worsening of your situation, you must come back to addressing all five points where possible, allowing them to take effect again.

4. Evaluate the Success of Your Five-Point Rescue Plan

When healthcare professionals see a patient, the first thing they do is to assess that patient.

When they see the person again, they reassess the situation to see if there has been an improvement.

Once you have established and lived your Five-Point Rescue Plan, you must do the same.

Determine whether it is working and improve it if necessary.

You become the expert.

Some of your points of rescue may have become second nature; some can be put to one side until needed again.

> Example
>
> When a patient is in great pain, they will usually perform a set of prescribed exercises religiously until they are seen again. As clinicians we can often predict that the patient is feeling better when they tell us that they have forgotten to do their exercises; the pain has lessened, and their need for that point has diminished.

If you do not achieve a positive result following the application of your five points of rescue then there are two possibilities;

- **The points you have selected may not be exactly right for you**

They may have initially seemed appropriate at the time of choosing, but, in applying them, you have noticed that they could be replaced with ones more suited to your needs.

This is all part of the process.

Let your plan evolve.

There may be different points which you find easier to apply or that you are more motivated to use.

If so, change your plan; once more preferable points are implemented, you will experience success.

You may need to brainstorm or enlist some help to come up with further rescue points.

This help can come from a number of sources: friends or family who know you well, health professionals who know you and your problem well, etc.

Try different combinations of points of rescue until you have the formula you need.

There is no right or wrong, only what works for you.

- **The problem you are addressing is clouded by another issue**

It may be that you are resisting the change for a number of reasons such as fear or lack of acceptance of your role in your situation.

Honesty is very important here.

Go back to identifying the problem, and if the problem is your resistance to change, then start with five points for that.

Often the problem which was initially described is clouded by difficulties in communication between those involved, due to the emotional nature of crisis situations.

If communication is an issue, then you need five points to address that, and so on.

At this point, we refer you to Chapter 3 in which we discuss barriers to the success of your Five-Point Rescue Plan in much further detail.

Well done!

You have done it.

You are now a Five Pointer!

Your plan should be simple and easy to implement.

However, as you become adept at using the technique you may find your plans become more complex.

You may begin to develop plans that overlap or plans which facilitate the Rescue Points for another plan.

The possibilities are endless.

You are now in control of your life and in possession of the skills you need to cope with anything and everything.

"We don't develop courage by being happy every day. We develop it by surviving difficult times and challenging adversity."

Barbara De Angelis

Chapter Three – Troubleshooting

As human beings, by nature we dislike change and are likely to resist it.

This next chapter describes the barriers that we have encountered when implementing The Five-Point Rescue Plan with our patients.

It is important to recognise this resistance and work to do something about it.

Resistance arises when we are in conflict.

Conflict can be considered as either internal or external.

Internal Conflict

Internal conflict is that which comes about because of our own thoughts and beliefs.

Having read the basic principles of the plan, it is likely that you are already examining the reasons why it may not work for you.

Examples:

I've always been like this, I can't change now.

I can't because of what happened to me in the past.

I'm too tired to start something new.

Taking up the plan won't change the outcome, x y z will still happen.

I've tried these things before, they never work for me.

I'm fine the way things are, I don't actually want to change.

My family/friends/colleagues won't like it.

If I change things, I'm afraid that x y z will happen.

I have a big problem to deal with; I couldn't possibly do this as well.

I have no will power and will never be able to see it through.

I can't change another person's behaviour; it is not my fault that they are doing this to me.

These statements are examples of internal conflict.

This is about what is going on in your head!

There may be internal conflict because of learned behaviour, because of our perceptions of others or because of what we feel we might gain from avoiding change.

Internal conflict due to learned behaviour

This is the reason that many people become stuck in situations from which it seems impossible to escape.

The barriers to improving a situation are often things which contributed to it in the first place.

Our brains are highly complex and still poorly understood.

We do know that we each have a unique internal model of the world.

This is a product of our genetic make-up and our life experiences.

As children, we learn the consequences of our

behaviour.

Those patterns of behaviour which keep us from harm and result in our getting what we need (such as love, attention, food, etc.) are processed and integrated internally.

As such they extend into adulthood and ultimately become habit.

They are also responsible for creating much of our circumstance.

Some patterns of behaviour that are learned in childhood are no longer helpful in our adult lives.

They create unwanted situations and must be replaced with something more suitable.

We know how we should be addressing a problem but changing our behaviour feels uncomfortable.

We have behaved in a certain way for our whole life, and it has got us this far; besides, we have no idea how to behave otherwise.

For example, a person who was praised as a child for finishing all the food on her plate at meal times may, as an adult, continue to feel the need to eat more food than is necessary to satisfy her hunger.

This, along with a host of other reasons, may contribute to her becoming overweight.

Although the obvious answer is to cut down on portion size and eat less food, it feels uncomfortable and goes against a lifetime of habit which (as far as the child who processed the behaviour is concerned) has got her this far unscathed!

Here is another example of how learned behaviour

can create barriers to the success of your Five-Point Rescue Plan:

As discussed in Chapter 2, when children trip and fall, they often look around to see who has noticed.

If no one has, they pick themselves up and run on.

If a parent has noticed they often cry and shout, revelling in the pain because they are rewarded with a hug and a kiss and attention from Mum or Dad.

In adults, this behaviour may still be present and can lead to unconscious attachment to a problem.

There is resistance to anything that may change the status quo because a positive outcome might result in the removal of something which the individual does not want to lose.

It takes time and a good deal of insight to break down this first type of internal conflict.

Rather than choosing points to tackle the consequence of learned behaviour, we would suggest that you go back to re-evaluate what the problem is.

Points to increase self-awareness, or techniques such as hypnotherapy, may have more success.

This is difficult to read.

As described above, we are all unconsciously attached to our problems.

This is perfectly normal; in fact, that is why they are problems to us in the first place.

We are unable to let go.

Something about the issue keeps us from moving forward.

This comes from fear.

What are you fearful of?

You can consciously choose to overcome this.

If you are thinking of closing the book now; stop!

Be brave, read on and become more enlightened.

Consider Bill's situation in Chapter 2:

When someone is in need, they are usually surrounded by family, friends and health professionals all trying to make things better for them.

If Bill creates a Five-Point Rescue Plan and moves forward, gaining control of his situation, he may no longer be deemed to require the previous level of support, and this may be removed.

This is obviously the preferred outcome, however, the support he has had may have felt like a comforting lifeline and the thought of it diminishing creates fear.

This can lead to unconscious self-sabotage which serves to keep things as they are.

Fear is the biggest barrier to the success of your Five-Point Rescue Plan.

Here are some of the things you may be fearful of:

- Confrontation – confronting the real problem, admitting there is an issue and taking ownership of it.

- Making change itself – making changes is difficult. For example reducing calorie intake involves hardship. Also, change may result in new problems occurring.

- Becoming a changed person – you have always behaved in a certain way, and it is hard to imagine being any different.

- Communication – whilst communicating is essential, it is also scary to talk honestly about your problem.

- Failure – of the plan and recurrence of the problem.

- Isolation – increased independence leading to decreased contact with others.

- Loss - loved ones, status, and esteem, money, function, form, independence.

If fear is preventing the success of your Five-Point Rescue Plan, you must recognise the source of it.

You must then create and implement a Five-

Point Rescue Plan to address the cause of your fear before you can move forward.

Do not let fear hold you prisoner.

The right actions always come from love and respect for yourself and others.

Internal conflict due to relationships with others

Remember that you are part of a complex network of relationships and you will have many roles.

You may be child, parent, sibling, partner, friend, colleague, patient, etc.

Clearly, our behaviour affects those around us and awareness of this can compound our problem and compromise and limit our choices.

You need to recognise this and incorporate it into your plan, rather than using it as a reason not to continue.

This is perhaps best illustrated using the example of a person with a terminal diagnosis.

In our experience, people sometimes struggle to tell loved ones about their diagnosis.

This is usually because they are afraid of upsetting them and worry about how they will react.

Everyone involved has high emotions and expresses them in different ways.

Everyone is wary of how others are feeling.

This can lead to a breakdown in communication.

A lack of communication in this situation is profoundly detrimental to all concerned.

Here, the first problem that needs to be addressed with a Five-Point Plan is communication.

Another example of how relationships with others might impinge on your Five-Point Rescue Plan is the presence of dependents.

If you have small children or elderly relatives who need your care and attention, then you need to recognise time as a limiting factor for you.

Either choose points that are quick and easy or, as parents ourselves, we would advise a Five-Point Rescue Plan to look at changing things to allow you some more time.

External Conflict

During the process we are describing, it is almost certain that you will encounter external conflict of some kind.

This is the conflict we find between individuals in a situation.

It is something to which the response depends entirely on the individual.

Some people shy away from confrontation whilst others react defensively with aggression.

You are probably aware, to some extent, of where you and others are on that spectrum.

- Human conflict is extremely complex.
- There is never a right or wrong side.
- We each have our own model of understanding

of the world and everything in it.

As discussed before, this is built up over time and much of it in childhood.

It comes from our continued processing and making sense of every experience we have.

It serves to enable us to instinctively choose how to behave in any situation.

It is our frame of reference.

Just as we each have our internal model of the world, we have our own version of the truth in every situation.

This is not likely to match that of others who are involved.

They have their own model of the world and

version of the truth.

Everything depends on our individual perspective in the circumstances.

This means that your vantage point is unique and will be coloured by many factors.

These factors will include emotional attachment to the outcome, individual memories of relevant events, long standing beliefs about the people involved and the situation itself.

For example, if you are ill your perspective may be affected by fear of the progression of your illness.

If your situation involves an argument that happened in the past, your recollection of events may be different to that of others.

If you believe one family member to be over-emotional and requiring much support on receiving bad news, this will affect your vantage point and ultimately how you deliver that news.

During external conflict, communication is usually compromised due to the high levels of emotion experienced by those affected.

It is difficult not to shout when you are angry or cry when you are upset.

During these times, it is hard to express yourself.

Remember that you cannot change the behaviour of other parties; the only thing you can change is your own behaviour.

If you perceive that someone is upsetting you, it is you who are upset.

Although the behaviour of that person is an external stimulus your response is entirely internal and the only thing you can control.

Stepping away from the emotion involved empowers you.

This enables you to understand your internal response, take control of it and improve the situation at hand.

Although it is difficult, you can absolutely choose to change what you think and how you feel.

How do you do this?

You simply choose to drop it and stop giving it your attention.

Stop feeding your negative feelings.

You will be amazed by how liberating this is.

You will be free.

Here are some practical tips on how to develop this skill.

- You could write your negative thoughts down on a piece of paper and throw it away or better yet burn it.
- Visualise your negative thoughts and feelings being erased.
- Listen to your negative thoughts and transmute them into beautiful music.

When you have dealt with your internal response to the external conflict, you can approach confrontation differently.

When all parties are experiencing internal conflict external conflict arises; the resolution is blocked and some "cooling down" time, however brief, may be required.

Mediation can also be very useful.

In our experience, there are very few people who actually enjoy genuine confrontation.

It is usually fear that underlies the aggression that leads to conflict.

During conflict, follow these steps

- Calmly give others time to express their viewpoints, allowing them to finish.
- Select an appropriate point in the conversation to respond. Interruption is counterproductive.
- Give yourself time to calmly speak your truth. Perspective is important here; there are as many versions of the truth as there are people in the discussion.

- If communication has broken down in such a way that people are shouting or talking at the same time as each other, suggest some time out. On resuming, encourage structured discussion, or ask someone to mediate.

- Come at everything from a position of respect however you feel about a person or their actions. As tempting as it may be to resort to cruelty, if you believe the argument to be legitimate and worthy of consideration, you will certainly damage your cause if you sink to sniping or keeping score. Any positive feelings resulting from point scoring will be short lived.

Remember to:

Come at everything from a position of respect at all times.

Respect yourself and your position.

Respect all other affected parties regardless of their behaviour.

Make this your mantra, and you will be able to take the heat of emotion out of an argument and speak your truth with dignity.

To Conclude

We have discussed the major barriers to the success of your Five-Point Rescue Plan.

There will be resistance throughout the process because it is part of our nature.

We must recognise it, empathise with ourselves, and move through it.

Regardless of how uncomfortable it makes you feel, ALWAYS ask yourself what you are gaining from the negative situation.

You can then implement your Five-Point Rescue Plan to generate a more positive outcome.

It is worth noting that you are likely to be your own most harsh critic.

We look to others to be kind and gentle with us in our situation, but we are usually not so forgiving towards ourselves when we mess up.

Remember that any backward steps along the journey are part of the process.

"Success is no accident. It is hard work, perseverance, learning, studying, sacrifice and most of all, love of what you are doing or learning to do."

Pele

Chapter Four

Example Five-Point Rescue Plan

Below are three examples of Five-Point Rescue Plans in action.

They will give you an idea of how to apply the methods discussed in the previous chapters.

Example One:

Jennifer is a physically active mother of two who has recently been diagnosed with degenerative changes in her lumbar spine following a comprehensive musculoskeletal assessment.

She is a teacher and on her feet a lot of the day.

She enjoys walking with her family and dogs, running and exercising at the gym.

She is in constant pain; this varies in intensity and is beginning to have an impact on her daily activities.

There is a twenty-four-hour pattern to her symptoms.

Her back is stiff and painful first thing in the morning; it eases off through the course of the morning then it aches again in the evening, after a day at work.

Identifying the problem

When Jennifer is asked what her problem is, she replies that she has a painful back.

This in itself is true, but we need to examine the situation in more depth for the plan to be situation specific.

Here we refer Jennifer to the questions we asked in the second chapter when identifying the problem.

Here are those questions with Jennifer's answers:

Why are you stuck?

I have been diagnosed with degenerative changes in my back and my back is painful.

Did something happen beyond your control?

Yes, I developed wear and tear in my back.

What are your limitations?

I can't change the fact that I have the condition.

I know that it is going to get worse and that I might need medical intervention in the future.

What stops you from moving forward?

I am upset about the fact that this will not get better and is likely to get worse.

I am afraid that we will no longer be able to go for long walks as a family which is a big part of what we do.

I am worried that, if I have to slow down, my children will suffer.

I am sad that I am not able to physically achieve the things that I used to such as charity fun runs and working out with my friends at the gym.

It is unfair; I have always had a healthy lifestyle and yet I am suffering with my health.

Who affects your situation?

My husband does not want to talk about the situation because he does not like to see that I am upset.

He worries about me being ill and potentially needing medical intervention in the future.

I think he thinks if we ignore it, it will go away.

I feel that he makes light of my condition because of this.

Our anxiety transfers to my children, and I feel that the subject is taboo.

Here are Jennifer's answers in table form:

What is my perceived problem?	Pain in my back.
What are my negative behaviours?	Worrying about the pain and focussing on it all the time.
What drives these behaviours?	Fear, anxiety, grief.
What are my limitations?	My diagnosis.
What can I change?	I can follow advice about treatments and stick to the exercises I have been given. I can change how I communicate with my husband. I can modify my activities to avoid pain.
What is my actual problem?	1. Poor communication with my husband. 2. Lack of pain control.

What do Jennifer's responses tell us?

From the answers that Jennifer gave, it is clear that the problem is more complicated than that of her painful back.

There is an issue of poor communication between family members, especially involving Jennifer and her husband, who clearly cares about her and could be a valuable source of support, when on board.

There are emotional issues around the fear of not being able to perform her maternal role well enough, and of losing friends and social activities.

She is also grieving for the part of herself which was able to perform all the physical activity she desired.

These are all emotive issues for Jennifer.

She has lost sight of the fact that, with some modifications to her lifestyle, she can still have these things.

She needs a Five-Point Rescue Plan!

We would initially suggest that Jennifer treats

communication with her husband as a separate problem which should be addressed before that of her painful back.

Jennifer is initially encouraged to come up with five points to address improvement in communication with her husband.

Remember; points are more likely to be effective if:

- They are relevant to her problem.
- They are easy to implement.
- They are 'old friends' which have been or are already utilised.
- They are easy to fit into her routine.

These are the points she chooses:

1. *Create social, fun time together away from the children providing some opportunities for us to talk in a relaxed environment.*

2. *Ask my husband to attend a clinic appointment*

with me to dispel his fears.

3. *Once we have discussed the degenerative changes to my satisfaction, agree to step away from the subject and make time for other activities.*

4. *Keep walking, as this is valuable family time, but shorten the distance.*

5. *Revisit fun activities we used to enjoy before my back became painful.*

Jennifer is encouraged to put these points into place gently and consistently and to note whether their communication improves in this area.

If it does not, she may need to review the points she has chosen.

She must then let go of the issue, in order to provide time and space for the changes to take effect.

Since Jennifer is in pain and affected emotionally by this, she is then encouraged to address the problem of her painful back.

Degenerative changes result from a wearing away of the discs and/or the articular cartilage in the joints of the back.

It is very common, and there is a wealth of advice available regarding its management.

Jennifer will have access to good advice, anti-inflammatory medication, and physiotherapy on the NHS.

There are also a great number of alternative therapies out there, so she has many options.

Lifestyle change should only need to be subtle at first, and those changes will help Jennifer to accept her prognosis and "tweak" her life accordingly.

Life-changing medical intervention is quite a long way down the line for her, and there are things that she can do in the meantime to make the best of her back and to keep it as healthy as possible.

It is not the "knell of death" that she initially fears it is.

Jennifer has seen a physiotherapist and gained some relief from her symptoms of pain.

During this session she found the application of heat to be effective.

She is taking anti-inflammatory medication as prescribed by her doctor.

She has been given a sheet of exercises which

are specific to her condition.

She has been told to avoid high-impact activities such as running.

With this in mind, these are her points:

1. *Do my back exercises twice a day.*
2. *Make changes to my posture when driving and sitting to reduce the stress on the joints in my back.*
3. *Continue to walk but shorten the distances and include additional family activities such as a meal together at the end.*
4. *Use therapeutic heat for pain relief and to reduce muscle spasm at home as part of my daily routine.*
5. *Take my medication when appropriate.*

Once these are in place, Jennifer is encouraged to emotionally let go of the issue.

She has taken action and no longer needs to constantly turn the problem around in her mind.

She can regain a sense of normality and some respite from the crisis.

There are, of course, many points that could be applied here, but these are the ones most relevant to Jennifer.

Another person with the same diagnosis might have completely different points.

It is our experience that a person such as Jennifer would begin to feel the benefit of taking control of her situation immediately.

She should be strongly encouraged to adhere to her points wherever possible.

Incorporating those activities that Jennifer

was fearful of losing into her Five-Point Plan, provides a constant reminder to her that, with some adjustment, she can still have them.

Additionally, there is an obvious positive effect on Jennifer's emotional state resulting from physical activity.

The presence of family based activity in point three relates directly to her previous difficulty with communication, and the two plans lend themselves well to running side by side.

Following her success, she will have a good supportive family environment, where everyone feels comfortable talking about the situation.

When success is experienced, it is natural for a person to forget and come a little away from their plan and points of rescue.

They are feeling better, and the need for rescue is diminished.

If, and when, that person experiences a return to the unwanted scenario, we gently encourage them to keep coming back to those points.

This is where the self-discipline comes in.

Example 2:

Alison is struggling to sleep.

She is a paralegal in a large firm and she has a heavy caseload.

She enjoys her job but recently she has been making mistakes and this has been commented upon by her manager.

She goes to bed at a reasonable time but finds she often lies awake until the early hours.

Her sleep is regularly broken throughout the night.

She wakes when her alarm goes off feeling unrefreshed and as tired as she was the night before.

She is anxious about not sleeping and what might be causing it.

She has been to see her GP who arranged some blood tests which were all normal.

Identify the problem

Alison feels her main problem is that she is tired all the time.

As with Jennifer, we need to examine the situation in more depth.

We take Alison through the steps of creating a Five-Point Plan.

Here are her responses.

Why are you stuck?

I am tired all the time and feel I have no energy for anything.

I can't be bothered with anyone or anything.

I haven't been out with friends for ages and I generally feel down.

Did something happen beyond your control?

The only thing I can think of is that eighteen months ago my mum was diagnosed with dementia.

She lives with my dad and he is caring for her; I am quite worried about both of them.

What are your limitations?

I can't change my mum's diagnosis, and I work

full time, so it is difficult to help Dad.

What stops you from moving forward?

I don't understand why I feel the way that I do.

I feel angry with myself for not coping with this situation.

It is Dad doing all the work not me and I am ashamed of myself for feeling low.

I am not the sort of person who can't cope.

I know I need to sleep, but when I get into bed my mind won't stop racing, and I lay awake worrying all the time.

I am also worried about work as it is a responsible job and I shouldn't make mistakes.

I don't know what to do or how to make these feelings go away.

Who affects your situation?

I am really worried about Mum.

She is not the person she used to be and she hardly recognises me.

I am starting to hate going to see her, but then I feel guilty for not being there.

I also feel guilty about not supporting Dad.

I have lovely friends, but I can't talk to them about how I feel because I am ashamed that I feel so low and don't want to look like I am moaning.

I am usually the strong one who helps everyone with their problems.

My manager has noticed some mistakes at work recently, and this has led to a warning.

I am normally very efficient and I am mortified about these mistakes.

I need to make sure this doesn't happen again.

I need to get some sleep.

Here are Alison's answers:

What is my perceived problem?	I cannot sleep.
What are my negative behaviours?	I lie awake at night worrying. I am not concentrating and I am not talking to people about my problems.
What drives these behaviours?	Anger, fear, guilt, self-loathing.
What are my limitations?	My mum's diagnosis. My job.
What can I change?	I can increase my knowledge. I can change my negative thought patterns. I can change my work.

What is my actual problem?	1. Lack of control. 2. Low mood and suppressing my feelings

What do Alison's responses tell us?

Alison has fixed on tiredness as her problem and she is keen to rectify this, however, it is clear from her answers that there is an underlying cause for her lack of sleep.

In fact, the poor sleep is a symptom of a deeper problem.

Low mood, lack of enjoyment of life (anhedonia) and poor sleep are the cardinal symptoms of depression.

Alison also describes feelings of helplessness, hopelessness, apathy, and loss of concentration.

She is clearly worried about her parents and has

some unresolved guilt issues around her feelings for her mum.

This is very common when a close relative develops dementia.

The relationship changes and everyone involved needs to adapt to this.

Alison is likely to feel the loss of her mum; this combined with her guilt about working full time and not being there can create quite negative feelings.

Unless these feelings are acknowledged and understood, they can break down a person's resilience and result in depression.

In addition to the worry about her parents, Alison is also worried about work.

Her symptoms are affecting her ability to do her job.

She is in a negative spiral of worrying about things; this makes her feel low and worthless and this, in turn, affects her sleep.

Her poor sleep impacts on her ability to cope with daily worries and round the spiral she goes again, getting lower and lower.

Alison's health beliefs are also important here.

She does not want to admit that she is low and feels she should be dealing with the situation.

She feels she is not the sort of person who gets depressed.

This kind of taboo around depression is very common and it must be acknowledged and taken into consideration in her Five-Point Rescue Plan.

Often people are afraid to talk about Mental Health issues as they feel they are lacking in some way because they feel low.

In fact, the more a person talks about their depression, the stronger they become.

Suppressing negative feelings and not addressing them is likely to manifest in an uncontrolled way that causes distress and more fear.

It can also manifest in physical symptoms.

Sometimes people feel more justified in talking about a physical pain, so their body creates one for them.

This is known as somatisation.

Alison needs to come to terms with her mum's diagnosis.

She needs to make sure her Dad is ok and has the help he needs.

She needs to talk to her friends and her colleagues, so they understand why she is acting the way she is.

In addition to these practical steps, she needs to consider treatments for her depression.

She needs a Five-Point Rescue Plan!

Remember; points are more likely to be effective if:
- They are relevant to her problem.
- They are easy to implement.
- They are 'old friends' which have been or are already utilised.

- They are easy to fit into her routine.

These are the points she chooses:

1. *I will find out more about dementia and look at support services for myself and my dad.*

2. *I will make an Occupational Health appointment at work and let them know about my mum and the way I have been feeling.*

3. *I will talk to my closest friends about what is happening to get their support.*

4. *I will use an online Cognitive Behavioural Therapy website for some self-directed CBT.*

5. *I will book a fun thing to do on a regular basis, to give myself things to look forward to and feel positive about.*

Often people assume that depression needs to be treated with medication.

In some cases this can be helpful, but not always.

There is a move towards talking therapies that help people develop better coping strategies.

Alison doesn't really like taking tablets, so even if she had been prescribed them, she would be unlikely to take them.

She did not choose to ask about medication as one of her points.

This works for her and will mean her plan is more likely to be successful.

Alison puts her points in place and does begin to see a lifting of her mood.

Her dad has been worried about her and realised something was wrong, but he has not wanted to ask.

They now talk regularly.

This is good for both of them as they are going through similar things.

The Dementia Admiral Service has introduced them to different ways of coping.

Alison is also surprised at how much better things are at work.

Her manager, Clare, has an aunt with dementia and understands what she is going through.

Clare arranges for a lighter workload and some time working from home so Alison can go with her parents to appointments.

Telling her friends results in a similar positive experience.

They help her come up with ideas for her fifth point, and so she has regular fun times.

The CBT helps Alison look at how she views the world.

It allows her to recognise that thoughts, feelings, and behaviours are interconnected.

When she is starting to feel low, she can now analyse her thoughts and feelings, pick out and discard the unhelpful ones, and concentrate on the positive ones which will result in positive behaviours.

Alison's sleep improves with her mood and she is soon back to full functioning at work.

Alison started with a physical symptom that was both a manifestation and a symptom of depression.

She sorted through the problem, analysing its component parts, and she put in place a practical plan to address her main concerns.

She took control of her situation and changed her life for the better.

Example Three:

Chrissie is suffering from eczema on her hands.

She is a physiotherapist and uses her hands all day coming into physical contact with patients.

She regularly washes her hands.

The skin breaks down leaving her susceptible to infection.

The condition is painful and unsightly and affects her performance at work.

She has creams to use but often forgets to apply them.

Identify the problem:

Chrissie feels that the main problem is that she

has eczema in her hands.

As with the previous examples, we have to examine the situation in more depth.

Why are you stuck?

The skin has broken down on my hands it is painful and unsightly and I cannot perform my job properly.

Did something happen beyond my control?

No, not that I can think of.

What are your limitations?

I have sensitive skin.

I have contact with other people's skin all day and I have to wash my hands all the time.

I am a busy working mum and so have little time for self-care.

What stops you moving forward?

Management of the situation takes time and effort and sometimes I don't have the time to look after my skin properly.

Who affects my situation?

I worry that patients are put off by the state of my hands.

My loved ones worry about my hands because I am in pain and vulnerable to infection.

Here are Chrissie's answers:

What is my perceived problem?	I have eczema.
What are my negative behaviours?	I ignore medical advice and forget to look after my hands.
What drives these behaviours?	Apathy.
What are my limitations?	Time and the need to wash my hands all the time at work.
What can I change?	My attitude.
What is my actual problem?	Lack of self-discipline.

What do Chrissie's responses tell us?

Chrissie is reluctant to take time away from her busy schedule to look after her skin.

She has already seen a dermatologist, and been given advice and treatments but finds it difficult to factor them into her busy life.

Her perceived problem is eczema.

Her negative behaviour is disregarding the medical advice, forgetting to apply the creams and down playing the importance of the health of her skin.

Her limitations are the nature of her job, her time constraints and an element of apathy.

She needs to value the health of her skin.

Her actual problem is a lack of self-discipline regarding her hand care.

She needs a Five-Point Rescue Plan!

Remember; points are more likely to be effective if:

- They are relevant to her problem.
- They are easy to implement.
- They are 'old friends' which have been or are already utilised.

- They are easy to fit into her routine.

These are the points she chooses:

1. *I will always wear rubber gloves when washing up.*

2. *I will always wear gloves outside in cold weather.*

3. *I will moisturise my hands every time I wash them.*

4. *I will apply my steroid cream twice a day when needed.*

5. *I will see my Doctor if my skin complaint gets out of control.*

Although Chrissie's actual problem was a lack of self-discipline, her points are treatments for eczema.

Here the act of creating a Five-Point Rescue Plan is what really motivated her and addressed the problem.

Regular implementation of Chrissie's Five-Points of Rescue broke the cycle of inflammation and allowed the skin on her hands to heal.

Sticking to her points and being mindful of the health of her skin prevented recurrence of the problem.

As you can see The Five-Point Rescue Plan can address a wide variety of problems from simple to complex.

There is no problem, large or small, that will not benefit from the creation and implementation of a Five-Point Rescue Plan.

"Change will not come if we wait for some other person, or if we wait for some other time. We are the ones we've been waiting for. We are the change that we seek."

Barack Obama

Chapter Five

Five-Point Rescue Plan Workbook

This section shows how your workbook might look.

Please feel free to copy the headings into a journal to help you through the step-by-step guide described above.

It will help you to get started.

This is the first step on your journey.

Please allow yourself plenty of space.

Chapter Four outlined three scenarios and illustrated how the Five-Point Rescue Plan has helped others.

Go through each step and use the rest of the

book as a guide.

Step 1. Identify the Problem

- Why am I stuck?
- Has something happened beyond my control?
- What are my limitations?
- What stops me moving forward?
- Who affects my situation?

Consolidate and simplify your answers with the help of the table:

What is my perceived problem?	
What are my negative behaviours?	
What drives these behaviours?	
What are my limitations?	
What can I change?	
What is my actual problem?	

Step 2. In choosing your points of rescue remember...

- To keep them relevant to you and your problem
- To make them easy to implement and sustainable
- They may be old Friends
- To make them easy to fit into a routine

My Five Points of Rescue are

1.

2

3.

4.

5.

Step 3. Implement the Rescue Plan

Use this space to note down how you are going to implement your Plan.

Things you may need and people who need to be

involved.

Also, use it as a log or diary to record how you are getting on.

Step 4. Reassess the Situation

Have you moved forward or not?

Your diary will come in handy here.

Do you need to refine your points?

Do you need to go back to identifying the problem?

Do you need to re-read Troubleshooting (Chapter 3)?

"You never change your life until you step out of your comfort zone; change begins at the end of your comfort zone."

Roy T. Bennett

Chapter Six

Portable Five-Point Plans

During our journey, we discovered a common obstacle to people moving forward with their Five-Point Rescue Plan was the difficulty encountered in adapting it to different environments.

For example, a person going on holiday may find it difficult to apply their specific points while away.

We discussed the idea of adapting their current plan to their new environment, but this proved to be rather overwhelming.

Changes in their environment were leading to increased anxiety and fear of the problem returning.

This was counter-productive.

In response to this, we developed the idea of a physical, portable Five-Point Rescue Pack.

In certain situations the pack could be taken along by its owner when out of their comfort zone.

This often proved to become part of the fun of holiday packing; the stress of the impending issue being replaced by the creation of a physical tool which would help to manage it.

Below are some examples of common Rescue Packs for various issues:

Stress
- Lavender Oil
- Squeezy stress ball
- St Johns Wort (check with your GP)
- Relaxation exercise sheet
- Notebook and pencil (to write down anxieties)

Pain

- Heat and/or Cold Pack
- Ibuprofen Gel (check with your GP)
- Exercise sheet
- Simple painkillers (check with your GP)
- TENS machine (check with your GP)

Menopause

- Exercise plan appropriate to the holiday venue
- Black Cohosh (check with GP)
- Evening Primrose oil capsules for breast tenderness
- CBT Moodgym APP
- HRT or Oestrogen Cream (check with your GP)

Insomnia

- Reduce caffeine intake
- Relaxation exercises before bed
- Lavender oil on the pillow
- Avoid technology before bed or use a blue

shade on the device
- Avoid day time napping

Exams

- Lucky Talisman (Chrissie's was a Hairy Highland Gonk; Karen's was a glass Whitby duck!)
- Favourite pen
- Packet of sweets
- Scented handkerchief
- Watch

Rescue packs can be made for all situations.

Think laterally, be creative and don't be daunted.

You can change them as you find new things that help and don't forget to share ideas with friends and family.

Whilst physical, portable rescue packs are

valuable; remember you are a ready-made rescue pack.

Here we have included a simple five-point relaxation exercise which, when practised, can be utilised anywhere and in any situation from a crowded train to a hospital interview room.

Five-Point Relaxation Exercise

In stressful situations, this is an excellent place to start.

Within a few minutes, you will have achieved a more relaxed state, enabling you to calmly take control of your thoughts and actions.

It is well worth perfecting this technique:

1. Slowly take three deep breaths. Try to make the out-breath a little longer than the in-

breath.

2. Take an imaginary trip around your body, relaxing the muscles in every body part as you go. Start at the toes and work your way up. If you find this difficult, it is often enough just to recognise where there is tension and to know that you intend to release it.

3. In your mind, take yourself to a place where you have felt truly at peace. It might be a previously visited holiday destination, a beautiful garden, a relaxing beach or a shady stream.

4. Affirm your positive thoughts and intentions here. You may wish to write them down first. Use positive language for example: "I will eat healthy wholesome food" rather than "I <u>will not</u> eat unhealthy food." "My head feels clear and I feel well today" rather than "I will not get a headache today." "I feel calm, serene and in control" rather than "I will not get anxious."

5. Gently bring yourself back to full awareness feeling refreshed, positive and in control.

There are many relaxation/meditation techniques available.

Find one that works for you.

In Summary:

We hope you have found this book empowering.

WE use Five-Point Rescue Plans in our own daily lives on a regular basis.

The Five-Point Rescue Plan forms the basis of all of our work with patients.

Here are some final words from people who we have helped.

"Whilst attending private physiotherapy sessions with Chrissie following an injury to my back, I was also suffering very badly with work related stress. The stress manifested itself through daily episodes of vomiting. It was debilitating, it was ruling my life and preventing my return to work. I had undergone medical tests through my GP and nothing was resolved however Chrissie suggested to me that I needed to use the Five-Step Plan to break the cycle. She went through the Five-Step Plan with me and helped me to decide what each step should consist of. To my surprise and delight over a few weeks, it worked well. Consistency was the key. I began to feel more in control. I began to recognise the signs of an 'attack' coming on and more often than not I managed to avert it using the techniques I had learned. I was finally able to return to work and a year on, despite still suffering from fluctuating stress levels, it has been months since I had a full blown 'attack'. Massive

thanks to Chrissie for sharing her knowledge!!"

Sarah, Ackworth

"I cannot thank Dr. Forshaw enough for the help that she has given me. Not only was I able to understand and relate to the rescue recovery plan, the personal 1:1 care I received from Dr. Forshaw was amazing, and has empowered me to take control of my life again. I felt like I could really open up and was really listened to, so much so I feel like I can share my learning with my family and help them understand my issues and their own. Thank you!"

Kayleigh, Doncaster

In June 2014 I took part in the Five-Point Plan with Christine Mowbray at Bell Lane Clinic.

This has given me continuing relief from pain and discomfort in the subsequent 3 years.

Phillip, Ackworth

You now hold the skills you need to help yourself in the palm of your hand.

You can take all you have learned from this book anywhere in the world.

Go out into the world.

Be brave.

Be positive.

Be confident.

Have self-control and clear intention.

Be healthy.

Be well.

Above all be happy.

Christine and Karen

"I did then what I knew how to do. Now that I know better, I do better."
Maya Angelou

"You can't stay in your corner of the forest waiting for others to come to you. You have to go to them sometimes."

A. A. Milne

Chapter Seven - Resources

Below are some useful resources if you want to do some more specific reading:

www.patient.co.uk

www.nhs.uk – NHS Choices

www.nhs.uk/oneyou - Public Health England campaign to help adults live more healthily

www.moodgym.anu.edu.au – Self-directed CBT

www.mind.org.uk – Mental Health Charity offering support and resources

www.cruse.org.uk – Bereavement support

www.relate.org.uk – Relationship counselling

www.britishpainsociety.org

www.macmillan.org.uk – Cancer support services

www.fmauk.org – UK Fibromyalgia charity

www.actionforme.org.uk   - M.E

www.migranetrust.org

www.mndassociation.org – Motor Neuron Disease Association

www.actionms.co.uk – Action MS (Multiple Sclerosis)

www.scope.org.uk

www.disbilityrights.org

www.arthritisresearchcampaign.co.uk

www.burningnightscrps.org – Complex Regional Pain Syndrome

www.alcoholics-anonymous.org.uk

www.samaritans.org

www.bigwhitewall.com – Safe online community for people who are anxious

www.talktofrank.com – drugs and alcohol support website

www.carersuk.org – Support for carers

Please note all links web-links were current at time of going to print.

Ask about peer support groups at your GP

surgery. If they do not have any, you could enquire about starting one.

Further Reading:

A Little Light on Spiritual Laws: Diana Cooper, Findhorn Press 2007

You Can Heal Your Life: Louise Hay, Hay House 1984

Women Who Run With the Wolves: Clarisa Pinkola Estes, Ballantine 1992

Ageless Body, Timeless Mind: Deepak Chopra, RIDER 1993

The Inner Consultation: Roger Neighbour, Radcliffe 2004

References

Miller, N. 1992. Behaviour to Brain to health. In: Samson, F and Adel, G. eds. *The Neurosciences: Paths of Discovery, I.* Boston: Birkhauser, pp. 283-305.